Favourite Melodies for Piano

The world's greatest music
Arranged by Alan Ridout

Kevin Mayhew

We hope you enjoy *Favourite Melodies for Piano*.
Further copies are available from your local music shop.

In case of difficulty, please contact the publisher direct:

The Sales Department
KEVIN MAYHEW LTD
Rattlesden
Bury St Edmunds
Suffolk IP30 0SZ

Phone 0449 737978
Fax 0449 737834

Please ask for our complete catalogue of outstanding Instrumental Music.

Front Cover: *The Poppy Field* by Percy Tarrant (d.1934).
Reproduced by kind permission of the Fine Art Photographic Library, London.

Cover designed by Juliette Clarke and Graham Johnstone.
Picture Research: Jane Rayson.

First published in Great Britain in 1993 by Kevin Mayhew Ltd.

© Copyright 1993 Kevin Mayhew Ltd.

ISBN 0 86209 390 2

All or part of these pieces have been arranged by Alan Ridout
and are the copyright of Kevin Mayhew Ltd.

Printed and bound in Great Britain.

Contents

TAMBOURIN

François Joseph Gossec (1734 - 1829)

BIST DU BEI MIR

Johann Sebastian Bach (1685 - 1750)

PLAISIR D'AMOUR

Giovanni Martini (1706 - 1784)

MINUET

Luigi Boccherini (1743 - 1805)

D.C. al Fine

ON WINGS OF SONG

Felix Mendelssohn (1809 - 1847)

LARGO

George Frideric Handel (1685 - 1759)

BALLET No.1 from 'Orpheus'

Christoph von Gluck (1714 - 1787)

WALTZ from 'Coppélia'

Léo Delibes (1836 - 1891)

Moderato

MELODY IN F

Anton Rubinstein (1829 - 1894)

NIMROD from 'Enigma Variations'

Edward Elgar (1857 - 1934)

I KNOW THAT MY REDEEMER LIVETH

George Frideric Handel (1685 - 1759)

ALLEGRO ASSAI

Johann Sebastian Bach (1685 - 1750)

30

LARGHETTO

George Frideric Handel (1685 - 1759)

SLEEP SONG from 'Hansel and Gretel'

Engelbert Humperdinck (1854 - 1921)

PIE JESU from Requiem

Gabriel Fauré (1845 - 1924)

GALOP from 'Orpheus in the Underworld'

Jacques Offenbach (1819 - 1880)

PANIS ANGELICUS

César Franck (1822 - 1890)

CRADLE SONG

Johannes Brahms (1833 - 1897)

Andante con moto

O FOR THE WINGS OF A DOVE

Felix Mendelssohn (1809 - 1847)

WHERE'ER YOU WALK

George Frideric Handel (1685 - 1759)

LA DONNA È MOBILE

Giuseppe Verdi (1813 - 1901)

Allegretto

THE SWAN from 'Carnival of the Animals'

Camille Saint-Saëns (1835 - 1921)

SOLEMN MELODY

Henry Walford Davies (1869 - 1941)

Lento espressivo

53

PIEDS EN L'AIR from 'Capriol Suite'

Peter Warlock (1894 - 1930)

SALUT D'AMOUR

Edward Elgar (1857 - 1934)

JESU, JOY OF MAN'S DESIRING

Johann Sebastian Bach (1685 - 1750)

SERENADE

Franz Schubert (1797 - 1828)

THE LAST ROSE OF SUMMER

Traditional Irish